Contents

Is this her pet?
Focus on: l as in *leg* 3

Fred's fish
Focus on: f as in *fan* 8

Off we go!
Focus on: ff, **ll** as in *puff*, *bell* 13

Ben and the cub
Focus on: b as in *bat* 18

Scan to listen along!
Audio to accompany this book can be streamed online with a mobile or tablet using this QR code:

About this book

These short stories are designed to give young children blending and reading practice. They are decodable, which means the words in them only include letter shapes and sounds that the children have learned. The stories also gradually introduce a few 'tricky' words, which are essential for children to become familiar with, such as 'they', 'of' and 'said'.

As children progress through these readers, new letter sounds and 'tricky' words are added and previous learning is revised. The progression links directly to the teaching order and lessons in the Letterland *Teacher's Guides* (UK and US versions). Each story begins with a title page that provides important information for children and teachers.

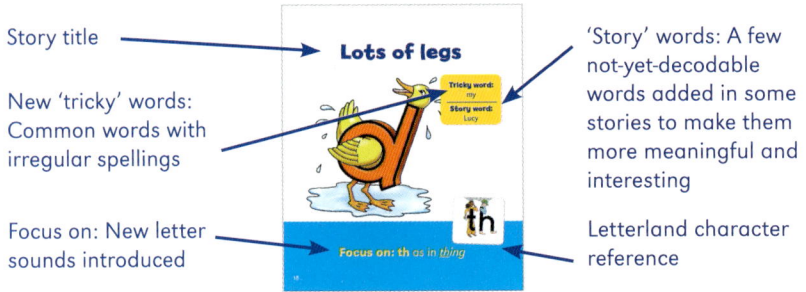

Story title

New 'tricky' words: Common words with irregular spellings

Focus on: New letter sounds introduced

'Story' words: A few not-yet-decodable words added in some stories to make them more meaningful and interesting

Letterland character reference

Basic teaching tips:

- Encourage the sounding out of decodable words (and any decodable parts of 'tricky' words).
- Discuss the stories with the children to ensure comprehension and engagement.
- Encourage re-reading in pairs or individually to develop fluency and reading for meaning.

See **www.letterland.com/Phonics-Readers** and the latest editions of the Letterland **Teacher's Guides** for more suggestions on how to use this book.

Is this her pet?

Tricky word: her

Focus on: l as in *leg*

Is this her pet on the log?

Can this pet sit on her lap?

Is that long, thin thing hers?

Yes, it is hers. She lit it up!
Can you see her pets?

Fred's fish

Focus on: f as in *f̲an*

Fred has lots of fish.

He fed them at ten.

He fits this fish in.

This fish has lots of big fins.

Off we go!

Tricky word: for

Focus on: **ff, ll** as in *puff, bell*

I am filling it up.

That bell is for us.

It tells us to get going.

We huff and puff up the hill.

We did it!

Ben and the cub

Tricky word: look

Focus on: b as in *bat*

Ben is looking for a cub.

Then he sees a cub.

Oh, no! This is bad! Look, Ben, can you see the cub's Mum?

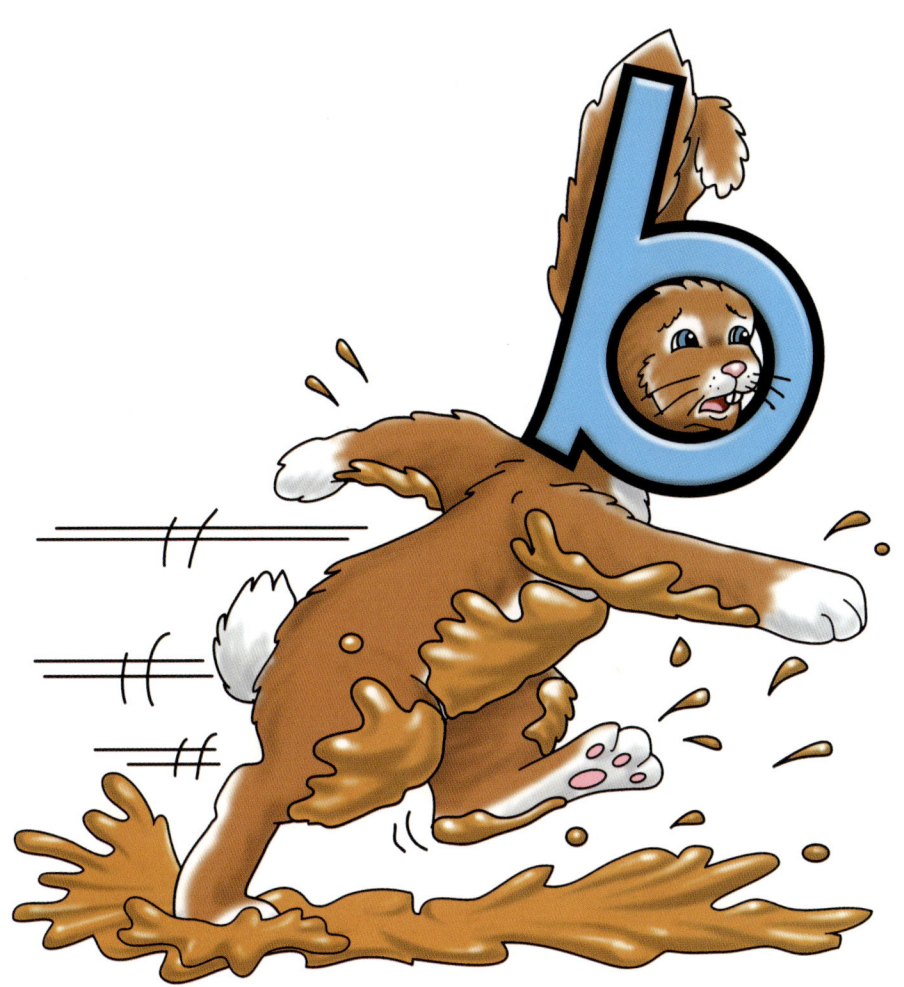

Ben sees her. Run, Ben, run!
He runs in the mud.

Look, Ben got the mud off! He is glad to be back in his tub!